2025 MOON CALENDAR

	1	2	3	4	5	6	7	8	9	10	11	12	13	14	15	16	17	18	19	20	21	22	23	24	25	26	27	28	29	30	31
JANUARY	WED	THR	FRI	SAT	SUN	MON	TUE	WED	THR	FRI	SAT	SUN	MON	TUE	WED	THR	FRI	SAT	SUN	MON	TUE	WED	THR	FRI	SAT	SUN	MON	TUE	WED	THR	FRI
FEBRUARY	SAT	SUN	MON	TUE	WED	THR	FRI	SAT	SUN	MON	TUE	WED	THR	FRI	SAT	SUN	MON	TUE	WED	THR	FRI	SAT	SUN	MON	TUE	WED	THR	FRI			
MARCH	SAT	SUN	MON	TUE	WED	THR	FRI	SAT	SUN	MON	TUE	WED	THR	FRI	SAT	SUN	MON	TUE	WED	THR	FRI	SAT	SUN	MON	TUE	WED	THR	FRI	SAT	SUN	MON
APRIL	TUE	WED	THR	FRI	SAT	SUN	MON	TUE	WED	THR	FRI	SAT	SUN	MON	TUE	WED	THR	FRI	SAT	SUN	MON	TUE	WED	THR	FRI	SAT	SUN	MON	TUE	WED	
MAY	THR	FRI	SAT	SUN	MON	TUE	WED	THR	FRI	SAT	SUN	MON	TUE	WED	THR	FRI	SAT	SUN	MON	TUE	WED	THR	FRI	SAT	SUN	MON	TUE	WED	THR	FRI	SAT
JUNE	SUN	MON	TUE	WED	THR	FRI	SAT	SUN	MON	TUE	WED	THR	FRI	SAT	SUN	MON	TUE	WED	THR	FRI	SAT	SUN	MON	TUE	WED	THR	FRI	SAT	SUN	MON	
JULY	TUE	WED	THR	FRI	SAT	SUN	MON	TUE	WED	THR	FRI	SAT	SUN	MON	TUE	WED	THR	FRI	SAT	SUN	MON	TUE	WED	THR	FRI	SAT	SUN	MON	TUE	WED	THR
AUGUST	FRI	SAT	SUN	MON	TUE	WED	THR	FRI	SAT	SUN	MON	TUE	WED	THR	FRI	SAT	SUN	MON	TUE	WED	THR	FRI	SAT	SUN	MON	TUE	WED	THR	FRI	SAT	SUN
SEPTEMBER	MON	TUE	WED	THR	FRI	SAT	SUN	MON	TUE	WED	THR	FRI	SAT	SUN	MON	TUE	WED	THR	FRI	SAT	SUN	MON	TUE	WED	THR	FRI	SAT	SUN	MON	TUE	
OCTOBER	WED	THR	FRI	SAT	SUN	MON	TUE	WED	THR	FRI	SAT	SUN	MON	TUE	WED	THR	FRI	SAT	SUN	MON	TUE	WED	THR	FRI	SAT	SUN	MON	TUE	WED	THR	FRI
NOVEMBER	SAT	SUN	MON	TUE	WED	THR	FRI	SAT	SUN	MON	TUE	WED	THR	FRI	SAT	SUN	MON	TUE	WED	THR	FRI	SAT	SUN	MON	TUE	WED	THR	FRI	SAT	SUN	
DECEMBER	MON	TUE	WED	THR	FRI	SAT	SUN	MON	TUE	WED	THR	FRI	SAT	SUN	MON	TUE	WED	THU	FRI	SAT	SUN	MON	TUE	WED	THU	FRI	SAT	SUN	MON	TUE	WED
	1	2	3	4	5	6	7	8	9	10	11	12	13	14	15	16	17	18	19	20	21	22	23	24	25	26	27	28	29	30	31

AF823135

THE EXPERIMENT

www.themooncalendar.com

New Moon
Full Moon
First Quarter Moon
Last Quarter Moon
Lunar Eclipse
Solar Eclipse

 Data provided by the US Naval Observatory.

All times are expressed on a 24-hour clock and in Universal Time (UT).

On a 24-hour clock, AM is from 00:00 (midnight) to 11:59, and PM is from 12:00 (noon) to 23:59. Universal Time is also known as Greenwich Mean Time. To convert to other time zones, use the guide below. Note that events marked with a * occur on the previous date in one or more of the North American time zones.

TIME ZONE CONVERSIONS		
	Eastern Standard	subtract 5 hours
	Central Standard	subtract 6 hours
	Mountain Standard	subtract 7 hours
	Pacific Standard	subtract 8 hours

DAYLIGHT SAVING TIME	BEGINS	ENDS	
North America	Mar 9	Nov 2	subtract 1 less hour than above
United Kingdom	Mar 30	Oct 26	add 1 hour

2025 PHASES OF THE MOON

LUNATION	NEW MOON	FIRST QUARTER	FULL MOON	LAST QUARTER
1262		Jan 6 23:56	Jan 13 22:27	Jan 21 20:31
1263	Jan 29 12:36	Feb 5 08:02	Feb 12 13:54	Feb 20 17:33
1264	*Feb 28 00:45	Mar 6 16:32	*Mar 14 06:55	Mar 22 11:29
1265	Mar 29 10:58	*Apr 5 02:15	*Apr 13 00:22	*Apr 21 01:36
1266	Apr 27 19:31	May 4 13:52	May 12 16:56	May 20 11:59
1267	*May 27 03:02	*Jun 3 03:41	*Jun 11 07:44	Jun 18 19:19
1268	Jun 25 10:32	Jul 2 19:30	Jul 10 20:37	*Jul 18 00:38
1269	Jul 24 19:11	Aug 1 12:41	*Aug 9 07:55	*Aug 16 05:12
1270	*Aug 23 06:07	*Aug 31 06:25	Sep 7 18:09	Sep 14 10:33
1271	Sep 21 19:54	Sep 29 23:54	*Oct 7 03:48	Oct 13 18:13
1272	Oct 21 12:25	Oct 29 16:21	Nov 5 13:19	*Nov 12 05:28
1273	*Nov 20 06:47	*Nov 28 06:59	Dec 4 23:14	Dec 11 20:52
1274	*Dec 20 01:43	Dec 27 19:10		

2025 ECLIPSES

***Mar 14.** *Total lunar.* Visible in parts of Antarctica, eastern Australia, western Africa, the Americas, Europe, Japan, eastern Russia, and the Atlantic and Pacific Oceans.

Mar 29. *Partial solar.* Visible in parts of Africa, most of Europe, Greenland, Iceland, extreme northeastern North America, northwestern Russia, and the northern Atlantic Ocean.

Sep 7. *Total lunar.* Visible in parts of Antarctica, Asia, Australasia, Europe, and the eastern Atlantic, Indian, and western Pacific Oceans.

Sep 21. *Partial solar.* Visible in western Antarctica, eastern Melanesia, New Zealand, and southern Polynesia.

	BEGINS	MIDDLE	ENDS
*Mar 14	03:56	06:59	10:02
Mar 29	08:51	10:48	12:44
Sep 7	15:27	18:12	20:57
Sep 21	17:30	19:42	21:54

2025 PERIGEE†	2025 APOGEE‡
Jan 7 23:36	*Jan 21 04:56
*Feb 2 02:44	*Feb 18 01:12
Mar 1 21:20	Mar 17 16:38
*Mar 30 05:27	Apr 13 22:49
Apr 27 16:16	*May 11 00:50
*May 26 01:38	Jun 7 10:44
*Jun 23 04:44	*Jul 5 02:30
Jul 20 13:54	Aug 1 20:38
Aug 14 18:02	Aug 29 15:35
Sep 10 12:11	Sep 26 09:47
Oct 8 12:37	Oct 23 23:32
+Nov 5 22:30	–*Nov 20 02:49
Dec 4 11:07	*Dec 17 06:11

† *Closest approach of the Moon to the Earth in a lunar month (lunation).*

‡ *Farthest distance from the Moon to the Earth in a lunar month (lunation).*

\+ *Closest approach of the year, also a "supermoon" as the Moon will be full.*

– *Farthest distance of the year.*

 THE EXPERIMENT and its colophon are registered trademarks of The Experiment, LLC. Printed in the USA. Distributed by W. W. Norton & Company. Distributed in Canada by University of Toronto Press Distribution, and in the UK by Melia Publishing Services, Ltd.

themooncalendar.com

THE EXPERIMENT ▪ NEW YORK

BECAUSE EVERY BOOK IS A TEST OF NEW IDEAS

theexperimentpublishing.com

theexperiment

$4.00 US / $5.00 CAN / £2.99 GBP

ISBN 978-1-891011-49-8

50400

9 781891 011498